Six in a Bed

Written by Roderick Hunt
Illustrated by Alex Brychta

Mum and Dad.

3

Mum, Kipper and Dad.

Mum, Kipper, Dad and Chip.

Biff, Mum, Kipper, Dad, Chip…

...and Floppy!

Talk about the story

Matching

Match the people with their belongings.

Get Dad!

Written by Roderick Hunt
Illustrated by Alex Brychta

Go on, Dad!

Get Biff.

Go on, Dad!

Get Chip.

Go on, Dad!

Get Kipper.

Go on, Mum!

Get Dad!

Talk about the story

What did Dad use to spray Biff?

How many different ways of making people wet can you remember?

Did Dad think he would get wet?

What do you like to play when it's hot?

Maze

Help the children get to Dad.